COLLECTOR'S ILLUSTRATED PRICE GUIDE

Dolls

WITH CURRENT VALUES

D1482466

Copyright: Bill Schroeder, 1977
ISBN 0-89145-039-4

COLLECTOR BOOKS
P.O. Box 3009
Paducah, Kentucky 42001

INTRODUCTION

Doll collecting has enjoyed a steady climb in popularity over the past few years until it is now at the point of being the third most popular collecting hobby in the world. Dolls come in all sizes and materials making this hobby one with many choices for the doll collector. This book has been divided into two main groups for the reader's convenience. The first group is made up of modern dolls, produced from 1935 until today. The second division is antique dolls, those produced prior to 1935.

It would be impossible to catalog a complete cross section of the collectible dolls available in a volume of this size. An attempt has been made here, to present an easy to use representative sampling of many kinds of dolls, both antique and modern. The doll enthusiast will find helpful information for identifying and pricing dolls.

The prices in this book are representative of retail values for the examples nation wide. The prices are for dolls in excellent condition without missing parts and without defacing marks or breaks. The reader should keep in mind that prices can be expected to increase and decrease in a realitively short time as collecting fads change and more collectors come into the scene. It is also important to remember that the prices here are what a dealer would ask for a doll rather than prices that a dealer might pay for the dolls.

The material in this book is from MODERN COLLECTOR'S DOLLS, MODERN COLLECTOR'S DOLLS SECOND SERIES, MODERN COLLECTOR'S DOLLS THIRD SERIES, ANTIQUE COLLECTOR'S DOLLS, and ANTIQUE COLLECTOR'S DOLLS SECOND SERIES, all by Patricia Smith.

The twelve books that make up the COLLECTOR'S PRICE GUIDE series are the result of a number of requests for an inexpensive series of books dealing with antiques and collectibles in several fields. The books are not intended to present a complete picture of each type of collectible but rather a representative sampling of the collectible, within space limitations, including an accurate current value.

Mattel - 11" "Twiggy". Same body as Francie. Snapping knees. Rooted short cut hair. Painted blue eyes/lashes. Open mouth with painted teeth. Dress not Mattel's. Marks: 1966/Mattel Inc/US Patented/US Pat. Pend./Made in/Japan. $9.00.

Alexander - 7" "Dionne Quints". All composition with molded painted brown hair. Painted side glancing brown eyes. Marks: Alexander on head Tags: Dionne Quint Doll. Original clothes. 1936. $125.00 per set.

Mollye - 20" "Irene Dunn". All composition. Stands on music box. Special human hair wig. All lace dress. This is one of the "Hollywood Cinema Fashions" by Mollye. She also designed stars such as Jeannette McDonald, Joan Crawford, Marilyn Monroe and many others. $125.00.

Roberta - 17" "Haleoke" From Arthur Godfrey Show. All hard plastic walker, head doesn't turn. Blue sleep eyes/lashes. Skin tones on head only are suntan. Glued on black saran hair. Marks: Made in U.S.A., on back. Clothes made in Hawaiian Islands, with Uke/shoes and hose extra. Dist. by Cast distributing Corp. NY. $45.00.

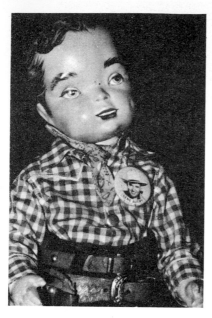

Terry Lee - 16" "Gene Autry" in Round Up outfit. All rigid plastic. Hand brush painted brown hair and eyebrows. Decal blue eyes. Painted teeth. Original. Gene Autry button. Marks: Terri Lee/Pat. Pending, on back. Shirt tag: Gene Autry. Was issued in two outfits, the other was: Rodeo (light pants and silk shirt). 1950. $165.00.

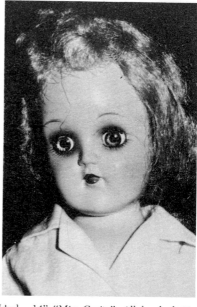

Ideal - 14" "Miss Curity". All hard plastic with glued on yellow saran wig. Blue sleep eyes/lashes. Eye shadow over and under eyes. Posable legs and arms. Original uniform. Marks: Ideal Doll/Made in USA, on head. Ideal Doll/P-90, on body. This is same body and head used for the Toni Doll. 1952. $25.00.

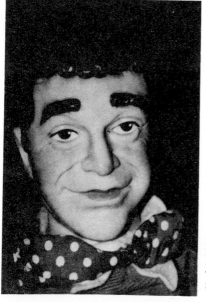

Knickerbacher - 13" "Soupy Sales". Vinyl head with cloth body and non-removable clothes. Marks: 1965 Knickerbacher, on head. Tag: Soupy Sales/1966 Soupy Sales, W.M.C. $35.00.

England - 5" "Beatles". Paul and George are all vinyl. Ringo and John are all hard plastic. Marks: The Beatles on back. NEMS/ENT.Ltd/ 1964 on one foot. Lic. By Seltaeb, Inc. on the other foot. $35.00 per set.

Remco - 4½" "Dave Clark" and 3" "Rick, Mike, Lenny & Dennis". The small ones are all plastic. Molded hair. All have open/closed mouths. No marks: Dave Clark: has vinyl head with rooted and lacquered hair. Painted teeth. Marks: Dave Clark/5/1964 Remco Inc., on back. 22/Dave Clark/1964/Remco Ind. Inc., on head. $22.00.

Puppet - 10" "Gene Autry" puppet. Cloth and rubber with molded on hat. Painted eyes. Marks: None on puppet. Box: National Mask &/Puppet Corp. $18.00.

Rag - 17" "Charlie Chaplin". All cloth with painted face. Wool hair. Floppy feet. Marks: Made By Louis Amberg & Son/Charlie Chaplin, on bottom of feet. Original clothes. $75.00.

Puppet - 30" "Charlie McCarthy". Cloth body, upper arms and feet. Plastic gauntlet hands. Plastic head. Painted features. Marks: Juro Novelty/1965. Original clothes. $50.00.

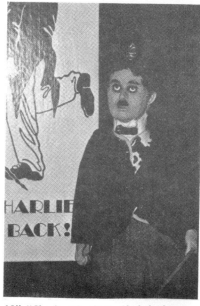

19" "Charlie Chaplin". Cloth body, arms and legs. Vinyl hands, feet (shoes) and head. Molded on vinyl hat. Painted features. Original removable clothes. Very well made and of good quality materials. Marks: Bubbles Inc/1972, on head. $45.00.

Mattel - 11½" "Miss America" Barbie doll. Walker, arms move and head turns. Original. 1972. Also offered for two box tops and $3.00 from Kelloggs Cornflakes. Marks: 1967 Mattel/US Pat. Pend./Taiwan. $8.00.

Kay Stan - 13½" "Terri Ann Meuson, Miss America 1971". Plastic and vinyl with rooted brown hair. Brown painted eyes. Dimples far out on cheeks. Original. Marks: Kaystan/1971, on head. Hong Kong, on body. Company plans on changing heads each year, to be a portrait series of beauty queens. $18.00.

Remco - 5½" "L.B.J.". All vinyl with molded on clothes. Painted features. Removable hat. Marks: 74/Remco Ind. Inc/1964, on head. $18.00.

Kamar - 13" "John F. Kennedy". Vinyl head, hands and shoes. "Wired" so that arms and legs can be posed. Sits in rocking chair. Reads newspaper with articles about wife, Jackie and children. A music box (key wound) plays and chair rocks. $22.00.

Vale - 14" "Rusty". All excellent quality early vinyl. Beautifully molded reddish/brown hair. Blue sleep eyes. Not original clothes. Marks: Vale/D.C., on head. From Danny Thomas Show "Make Room For Daddy". 1954. Sold as "Alden's Cuddliest" in 1952. $12.00.

Hong Kong - 11½" "Texaco Cheerleader". Plastic and vinyl with rooted yellow blonde hair. Painted blue eyes. Palms down. Tiny high heel feet. Original. Sold as premium with oil change at Texaco stations. 1973. Marks: 56/Hong Kong, on head. Hong Kong, on back. $5.00.

Eegee - 17" "Miss Sunbeam". Plastic body and legs. Vinyl arms and head with rooted yellow hair. Blue sleep eyes. Open/closed mouth with molded, painted teeth. Dimples. Original dress. Marks: Eegee, on head. Miss Sunbeam, on apron. $10.00.

Ideal - 18" "Harriet Hubbard Ayers". Hard plastic body and legs. Early vinyl "Magic Flesh" arms and head. Blonde glued on wig over hole in top of head that is stuffed. Blue sleep eyes/lashes. Marks: MK-18/Ideal Doll on head. Ideal Doll on body. 1953. $45.00.

Mattel - 11½" "Truly Scrumptious" (Talking) 1968. Marks: 1967/Mattel Inc/US & Foreign/Pats Pend/Mexico, on back. Genuine Truly Scrumptious/By Mattel, on wrist paper tag. Truly Scrumptious/1968 Glendrose Prod. Ltd/and Warfield Prod. Ltd/Made in Japan/1968 Mattel Inc. $9.00.

Unknown - 11½" "Carole Channing" as Hello Dolly. Plastic and vinyl with rooted orange/blonde hair. Painted eyes. Original. Marks: AE, on head. 1971. $5.00.

Rag - 27" "Lucy Arnez". All cloth. Plastic face mask. Orange yarn hair. Painted features. Marks: Apron: I love Lucy/Desi. 1953. $18.00.

Natural - 14" "Linda Williams". Plastic body and legs. Vinyl arms and head. Rooted dark brown hair. Blue sleep eyes/lashes. Open/closed mouth with six painted teeth. Open hands with extended little fingers. Marks: Linda Williams, on head. 1959. $12.00.

Shindana - 16" "Flip Wilson - Geraldine".
Foam stuffed cloth covered. Pull string
talker. Marks: 1970/Street Corner Productions Inc/Operation Bootstrap Inc/Los
Angeles, Calif. 90001/Skin Made in Taiwan.
1970. $22.00.

Mattel - 22½" "Doctor Doolittle". Cloth body
with sewn on clothes. Vinyl head with molded
hair and painted features. Pull string operated.
Says things such as "I talk with animals all
over the world". Marks: Dr. Doolittle/M-
CMLXVII Twentieth Century Fox/Film Corp.
Inc. $18.00.

Mattel - 6" "Doctor Doolittle". All vinyl with
molded hair and painted features. Marks:
1967/Mattel Inc./Japan. $10.00.

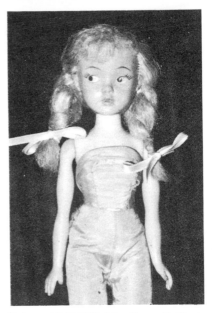

Mattel - 10" "Buffie". Plastic body. Vinyl arms, legs and head. Rooted blonde hair. Painted blue eyes. Open mouth with two painted teeth. Freckles. Open hands with left index extended. Marks: 1967 Mattel Inc/US & For/Pats. Pend/Mexico. 3½" Mrs. Beasley. $10.00.

Unique - 11½" "Ellie Mae Clampet". Plastic and vinyl. Rooted blonde hair. Painted blue eyes. Original clothes. Same doll used for Kellogs Corn Flakes in 1964, called "Calico Lassie". Ideal made these dolls for Unique. Marks: Unique, on head. $4.00.

Valentine - 14" "Roxanne". All hard plastic walker, head turns. Glued on saran hair. Blue sleep eyes. Open mouth, 4 upper teeth. Original. Marks: Made in USA/Pat. Pending, on back. Tag: Fashioned after the glamorous hostess of TV "Beat The Clock" program. 1953. $25.00.

Star Doll Co. - 14" "Dorothy Collins". All hard plastic with glued on yellow hair. Blue sleep eyes. Walker, head turns. Marks: 14, on head. Made IN USA, on back. 1954. $25.00.

11

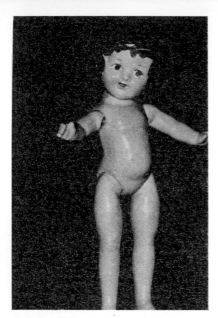

Arranbee - 8½" "Carolyn Lee". Black painted molded hair. Smile/closed mouth. 5 year old played in Virginia with Fred McMurray and Madelaine Carroll. 1941. Arranbee also produced sets of five labeled "Quint." Doll also used for "Round World" series. Marks: R&B/Doll Co., on backs. $22.00.

Doll Artist - 15" "Liz Taylor" By Lita Wilson. Bisque head, arms and legs. Cloth body. Glued on black wig. Painted features. Ring on left hand. Marks: Petite Portraits, on front of neck plate. Liz Taylor, on back with LW in corner. $105.00.

Cloth - 16" "Poncho" (Of Cisco Kid, Played by Leo Carrillo). Cloth with highly painted buckram face mask. Hat missing. ca. 1944. $75.00.

Dutchess - 7½" "Mary Hartline". All hard plastic. Felt clothes. Mohair wig. Blue sleep eyes. Original. $10.00.

Uneeda - 14" "Rita Hayworth As Carmen".
All composition with glued on red mohair wig.
Adult figure. Stapled on under clothes.
Original clothes. Marks: None. Tag & Box:
The Carmen Doll/W I Gould & Co., Inc./Inspired By Rita. $125.00.

Valentine - 14" "Luann Simms". All hard
plastic with knee length dark hair. Blue sleep
eyes. Walker. From Arthur Godfrey's TV
Show. Original dress. Marks: Made in
USA/Pat. Pend., on back. $30.00.

Joy Doll - 14½" "Marlene Dietrich". All composition. No molded hair under wig. Blue sleep
eyes. Stapled on clothes. Golden blonde
mohair wig. Gold dress/white net shawl. Deep
purple flower on top and in hair. 1945.
$45.00.

Valentine - 19" "Debbie Reynolds". As grown
up "Tammy". All hard plastic. Open mouth/5
teeth. Blue sleep eyes. Red lips/nails. Walker,
head turns. Mid high heel feet. Jointed knees/
ankles. Pale golden blonde hair glued on.
Marks: Made in U.S.A., back. Medium blue on
pale blue/white lace trim. $8.00.

Ideal - 15" "Mary Hartline". All hard plastic with glued on blonde wig. Blue sleep eyes. Eyeshadow over and under eyes. Original clothes. Marks: Ideal USA, head. Ideal Doll/P91, on back. 1952. $25.00.

Ideal - 18" "Judy Garland". As Dorothy of the Wizard of Oz. All composition with glued on human hair. Hair is a red/brown. Brown sleep eyes. Open mouth with six teeth. Original dress. Marks: Ideal Doll, on head. 18/Ideal Doll/Made in USA, on back. 11/18, on upper left arm. 10, on upper arm. 18, inside both legs. Paper dress tag: 17. 1939. $85.00.

Effanbee - 20" "Anne Shirley/Little Lady". Composition body, legs and head. Hard rubber arms. Glued on blonde human hair wig. Marks: Effanbee/USA, on head. Effanbee/Anne Shirley, on back. Ettanbee durable doll, on wrist tag. 1939. Original clothes. $25.00.

Junel - 11" "Mary Lincoln". All composition. Fully jointed. Painted blue eyes to side. Both arms fairly straight. Original deep blue velvet dress/gold trim. Tag: Copy of Dress worn by Mary Lincoln 1861/Junel Novelties Inc. NY. $18.00.

Ideal - 7" "Evel Knievel". All vinyl. Completely bendable. Plastic hands and feet/shoes, inserted by plastic rods so they are "jointed". Molded hair. Painted features. An original outfit (came in three). Marks: 1972 Ideal, in oval/Hong Kong, on hip. $4.00.

Hasbro - 4" "Monkee". All vinyl. Rooted hair. Painted features. Original. Marks: 1967/Hasbro/Hong Kong. $4.00.

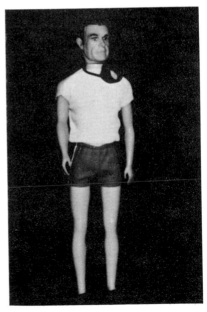

Ideal - 12½" "Illya Kuryakin, #2 Man From U.N.C.L.E.". Plastic body and legs. Vinyl arms and head. Molded blonde hair. Painted features. Marks: K-99 on head. Clothes Tag: Made In Spain. 1965. Illya Kuryakin was portrayed by David McCallum on the NBC-TV show "Man from U.N.C.L.E. 1965. $30.00.

Ideal - 12½" "007 - James Bond". Plastic body and legs. Vinyl arms and head. Molded hair. Painted eyes. Open hands with right toward body (arms snap up) to hold gun and other accessories. Marks: Ideal Toy Corp/B-12½-2. 1965. Mfg'd for A.C. Gilbert Co. $30.00.

Alexander - 8" "Princess Ann". All hard plastic with brown glued on wig. Blue sleep eyes. Jointed knees. Marks: Alex., on body 1957. $18.00.

Doll Artist - 20" "Queen Elizabeth". Signed Rene. 1959. $175.00.

Doll Artist - 28" "W.C. Fields" By Maxine Clasen. Composition head and hands. Wire armiture, bendable body. $165.00.

Alexander - 14" "Jenny Lind & Her Listening Cat". Marks: Jenny Lind/By Madame Alexander. 1969. $30.00.

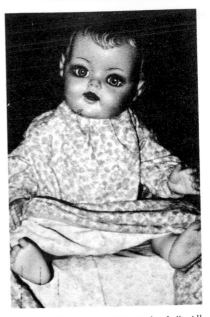

Alexander - 8" "Bonnie Prince Charles". All hard plastic with glued on blonde hair. Blue sleep eyes/molded lashes. Jointed knees walker. Original clothes, minus jacket. Marks: Alex, on back Tag: Alexander-Kins/By Madame Alexander. 1957. $20.00.

American Character - 21" "Ricky Jr.". All vinyl with molded hair. Blue sleep eyes. Open mouth/nurser. Marks: Amer. Char. Doll. on neck. 1956. $25.00.

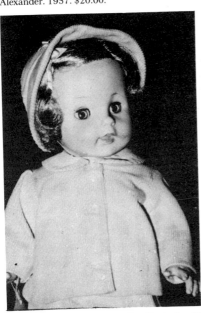

Alexander - 14" "Caroline". All vinyl with rooted blonde hair. Blue sleep eyes. Open/closed mouth. Original. Marks: Alexander/1961, on head. Alex. 1959/13,. on back. Caroline/Madame Alexander, on tag. $65.00.

Alexander - 15" "Princess Elizabeth". All composition with glued on human hair wig. Blue sleep eyes/lashes. Open mouth with 4 teeth that are individually spaced. 2nd and 3rd fingers molded together. Hazy eye shadow. Marks: Princess Elizabeth/Alexander Doll Co., on head. 1939. $35.00.

21" "Scarlett" 1966.
Roberta Lago. $95.00.

Citro - 25" "Polly Pond's Beauty Doll". One piece vinyl. Wire through legs so posable. High heels. Stuffed vinyl head. Saran hair. Blue sleep eyes. Pierced. Original. Came with Pond's face cream, etc. Sold for $21.95 in 1956. Marks: 4505, high on center crown. 1325-1/Made in USA, on neck flange. Tag: Polly Pond's Beauty Doll, Dressed in Daytime Ensemble. Citro Mfg. Co. $18.00.

21" "Betty Grable". All composition with glued on blonde mohair wig. Blue sleep eyes/lashes. Closed mouth. Posable legs. Marks: 22 over 8 under arms. 22 back of legs. This doll has been shown at doll conventions as Betty Grable but unless one is found with tag, this is uncertain. Original dress. 1940's. $45.00.

14" "Mary Martin" ca. 1950.
Carrie Perkins. $50.00.

Arranbee - 21" "Sonja Henie". All composition with glued on blonde mohair wig. Brown sleep eyes/lashes. Black eye shadow. Closed mouth. 2nd and 3rd fingers molded together. Marks: R & B on head. Original clothes. 1945. $35.00.

Alexander - 14" "Sonja Henie". All composition with blonde mohair wig. Brown sleep eyes/lashes. Dimples. Open mouth with four teeth. Marks: Madame Alexander/Sonja/Henie on head. 1941. $45.00.

Alexander - 14" "Scarlett O'Hara". All composition with glued on black wig. Sleep eyes/lashes. Closed mouth. Original clothes. Marks: Mme. Alexander on head. Dress Tag: Madame Alexander/New York USA. 1942. $65.00.

Alexander - 13" "Shari Lewis". Rigid vinyl body and legs. Soft vinyl arms and head. Brown glued on wig. Green sleep eyes/lashes. Marks: 1958/Alexander, on head. $50.00

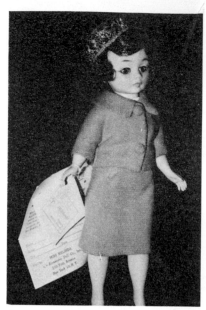

Alexander - 17" "Jane Withers". All composition with glued on brown wig. Sleep green eyes. Open mouth with four teeth. Marks: 17, on back. 1936. $75.00.

Alexander - 10" "Jacqueline". All hard plastic with glued on brown wig. Blue sleep eyes, blue eye shadow. Jointed knees. Original clothes. Marks: Mme/Alexander, on back. 1962. $28.00.

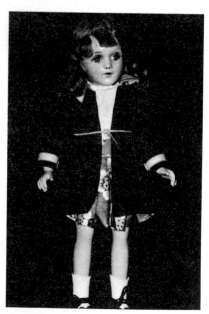

Arranbee - 17" "Gloria Jean". 1940. To help promote her new movie "A Little Bit of Heaven." Eyes are special on this doll. A very vivid blue. Clothes are not original. $65.00.

American Character - 8" "Ben Cartwright". All solid vinyl. Molded gray hair. Painted features. Jointed elbows, wrists, knees. Feet turn. molded on basis clothes. marks: A Large "C"/American Character, center of back. 1966. $25.00.

Doll Artist - 22" "Dick Clark". Bisque head with cloth body. Composition hands. Marks: None. The workmanship of the doll is outstanding, it is unfortunate we do not know the artist who made him. $165.00.

Amsco - 12" "Buffy" (T.V. series.) Make up and hairdressing head. Marks: 1971/Amsco Ind. Inc. Hopefully "Buffy" will look like this as a young woman, as the head is much too old looking for a child star. $35.00.

17" "Hedy Lamarr". All hard plastic. Black Saran hair, curls drop down neck. Not original clothes. Doll was to have been issued with the 1949 movie "Samson & Delilah." Not confirmed by Alexander Doll Co. $60.00.

Eegee - 17" "Gigi Perreaux". Hard plastic body, arms and legs. Early vinyl head with glued on dark brown hair. Brown sleep eyes/lashes. Open mouth with painted teeth. Feathered eyebrows. Marks: E.G., on head. 1951. Child Actress, licensed to Goldberger to make doll. $35.00.

Doll Artist - 18" "Paul Laurence Dunbar" (1872-1906). Often known as the poet of the people, he wrote in both Negro dialect and conventional English and also authored many works of prose. Marks: Bertabels Dolls-1965. The doll was designed by Roberta Bell N.I.A.D.A. artist. $265.00.

Cloth - 18" "Tiny Tim". All cloth with felt features. Body and limbs are wired for posing. Tag: Tiny Tim, on jacket. $18.00.

19" "Capt. Kangaroo". Cloth stuffed with vinyl head and painted features. Marks: 1961 Robt. Keeshan/Assoc. Inc. $25.00.

Mollye - 15" "Sabu" of the "Thief of Bagdad". All composition. Doll and clothes designed by Mollye. $165.00.

Ideal - 12" "Samantha, The Witch". Plastic and vinyl with rooted white hair. Green eyes looking straight ahead. Knees do not bend. Original dress, minus hat and broom. Marks: Ideal Tov corp/M-12-E-2, on head. 1965/Ideal (in oval)/M-12, on hip with a 1, lower down. $8.00.

Gilbert - 11½" "Honeywest". Plastic and vinyl with rooted blonde hair. Painted features. Original. Marks: K99, on head. Made by Gilbert Toys 1965. $10.00.

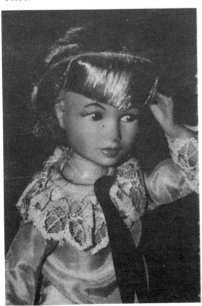

Horsman - 12" "Patty Duke". Posable arms and legs. Blue eyes to side (painted). An Irene Szor design. 1965. Marks: Horsman Dol/6211. $16.00.

Libby - 20" "I Dream Of Jeannie" as portrayed by Barbara Eden. Plastic and vinyl with rooted, frosted blonde hair. Blue sleep eyes. Original clothes. Marks: 4/1966/Libby, on head. Box: Sidney Sheldon Productions Inc. 1966/Libby Majorette Doll Corp/Exclusive Mfg. $18.00.

Ideal - 17" "Shirley Temple". All composition with glued on blonde mohair wig. Green sleep eyes/lashes. Open mouth with six teeth. Marks: Ideal, on head. $55.00.

Ideal 15" "Shirley Temple". All vinyl with rooted blonde hair. Brown sleep eyes/lashes. Open mouth with four teeth. Marks: Ideal Doll ST-15, on back and head. 1958. $18.00.

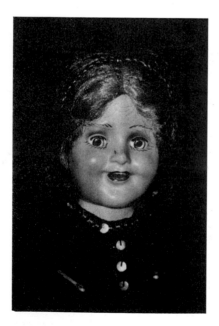

Canada - 14" "Barbara Ann Scott". All composition. Blue sleep eyes. Open mouth with six teeth. Marks: Reliable of Canada. $75.00.

Ideal - 17" "Shirley Temple Baby". All composition with glued on blonde mohair wig. Brown flirty eyes, sleep/lashes. Open mouth with two upper and three lower teeth. Marks: Shirley Temple, on head. $120.00.

Hasbro - 5" "Flying Nun". All vinyl with rooted hair and painted features. Title role on T.V. was played by Sally Fields. marks: 1967/ Hasbro/ Hong Kong. Original $7.00.

Horsman - 12" "Mary Poppins". Plastic body and legs. Vinyl arms and head. Rooted black hair. Side glancing blue eyes. Marks: H, on head. 1964. Mary Poppins was played by Julie Andrews in the 1964 movie of P.L. Traver's story. Walt Disney Productions. $18.00.

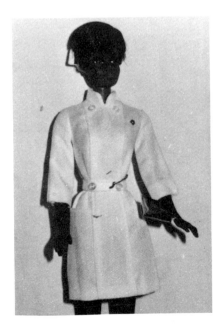

Mattel - 11½" "Julia". All vinyl with bendable knees. Rooted black hair. Painted brown eyes. Marks: 1966/Mattel Inc. Original clothes. From TV program "Julia" played by Dianne Carroll. $7.00

Ideal - 17" "Deanna Durbin". All composition with glued on dark brown wig. Brown sleep eyes/lashes. Dark grey eye shadow. Open mouth with felt tongue and five teeth. Dimples far out on cheeks. Marks: Deanna Durbin/Ideal Toy Co. on head. 1939. $75.00.

Bauer & Black - 21" "Miss Curity". All composition. Blue sleep eyes. Original. 1946. $35.00.

Ideal - 7" "Miss Curity". All hard plastic with one piece body and legs. Painted on stockings and shoes. Open hands with 2nd and 3rd fingers curled. Glued on blonde saran hair. Sleep blue eyes/painted lashes. Closed mouth. Uniform and cap made of thin oilcloth. Marks: None. 1953. Trademark Kendall Co. Original clothes. $7.00.

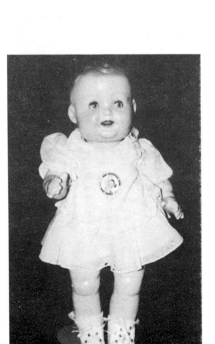

Freundlich, Ralph - 16" "Sandy Henville". Child movie star. All composition. Sleep eyes/lashes. Open mouth. Molded hair. All original including pin. $85.00.

Imperial Crown - 23" "Miss Pepsodent". All vinyl. Blue sleep eyes. Open mouth with rolling teeth. When laying down teeth are yellow, when sitting up, they rotate to white. All original. $45.00.

Puppet - 11" "Oliver Hardy". Cloth body puppet. Vinyl head with molded on hat. Marks: Knicherbacher/1965/Japan, on head. Licensed by Harmon Pic. Corp. $5.00.

Mary Hoyer - 14" "Olga" Skating outfit. This is the hard plastic Mary Hoyer doll. 1950. $25.00.

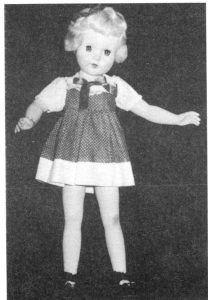

Effanbee - 18" "Tintair". All hard plastic. White glued on dynel wig. Blue sleep eyes/lashes. Open/closed mouth. Open hands all fingers curled. Marks: Effanbee, on head. Effanbee, on back. 1951. (Courtesy Montgomery Ward 1951 Catalog). Also sold as Honey and Honey Walker for a number of years. $40.00.

Mary Hoyer - 14" "Julianna" also "Sonja". Each outfit had a different name although the doll was the same. All composition with glued on brown hair. Blue sleep eyes. Light cheek dimples. Marks: The Mary Hoyer Doll, on back. Tag: Made/By/Mary Hoyer/Yarns. 1947. $35.00.

Uneeda - 36" "Betsy McCall". Plastic and vinyl. Blue sleep eyes. Original dress. marks: McCall Corp/1959, on head. Companion boy doll is "Sandy McCall." $45.00.

Uneeda - 11½" "Betsy McCall". Plastic and vinyl with rooted light red hair. Small brown sleep eyes. Posable head. Original. Marks: none. Made by Uneeda Doll Co. $15.00.

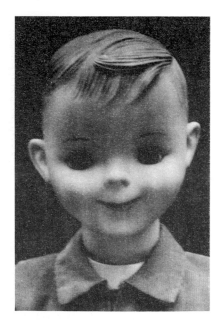

Ideal - 36" "Sandy McCall". Molded hair. Sleep eyes. Marked On Head: McCall/Corp 1959. $75.00.

H.D. Lee - 13" "Buddy Lee". All hard plastic made in one piece body, legs and head. Molded painted hair. Painted black eyes side glancing. Painted on cowboy boots. Trademark doll for H.D. Lee Co. Clothes were made in Lee Plant. Hats were made by outside source. Marks: Buddy Lee on back. 1949. $35.00.

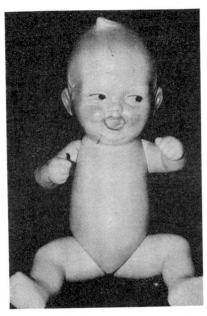

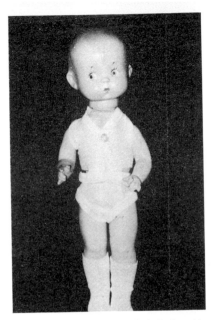

Germany - 6" "Baby Sandy" (Sandra Henville). Painted bisque. Blue painted eyes. Open/closed mouth. Dimples. (Marks: Germany, on back. $65.00.

Effanbee - 14" "Skippy". Cloth body with composition head and limbs. Wood block neck. Molded hair with one lock down forehead. Marks: Skippy/Effanbee. $55.00.

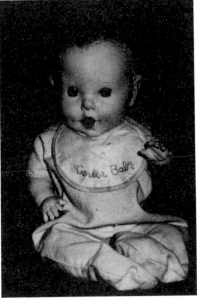

13½" "Kleenex Baby". Rigid vinyl body, arms and legs. Vinyl head with molded hair. Large blue sleep eyes/lashes. Open mouth/nurser. Open hands, palms facing body. Dimpled knees. Marks: Cannot make it out. 1958. $3.00.

Sun Rubber - 11" "Gerber Baby". All rubber with molded hair, painted brown. Inset stationary eyes. Open mouth/nurser. Dimpled cheeks. Crossed baby legs. Marks: Gerber Baby/Gerber Products Co, on head. Mfd By/ The Sun Rubber Co/Barberton, Ohio USA/Pat No, covered by squeeker, on body. 1956. $9.00.

American Character - 14" "Betsy McCall". Rigid vinyl body and legs. Vinyl arms and head. Rooted black hair. Blue sleep eyes/lashes. 2nd and 3rd fingers molded together. Medium high heel feet. 1961. $12.00.

American Character - 8" "Teeny Betsy McCall". All hard plastic with a creamy bisque finish. Rooted dark brown hair set in a skull cap and cap glued to head. Blue sleep eyes/molded lashes. Closed mouth. Mark: Center of back. in a circle: McCall Corp. 1958. Original dress. $15.00.

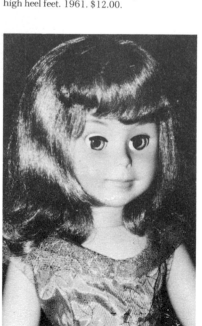

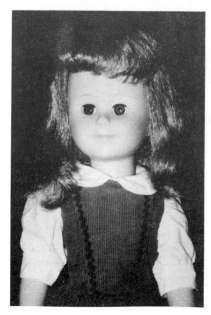

Uneeda - 29" "Betsy McCall". Plastic and vinyl. Jointed waist and legs high near hip joint. jointed ankles, wrist. Rooted blonde hair. Blue sleep eyes. Marks: McCall/1961/Corp. in circle. $30.00.

Uneeda - 22" "Betsy McCall". Plastic and vinyl. Jointed waist, wrist and ankles. Brown sleep eyes. Original clothes. Marks: none. $22.00.

Ideal - 18" "Miss Revlon". Dressed in "Cherries Ala Mode" outfit. Marks: Ideal Doll/VT-18. 1955. $22.00.

Ideal - 21" "Toni Walker". All hard plastic with glued on black nylon wig. Green sleep eyes/lashes. Eye shadow. Marks: P-93 Ideal Doll Made In USA on head. Ideal Doll/P-93, on body. 1950. $22.00.

Ideal - 10½" "Little Miss Revlon". Plastic and vinyl. Jointed waist. Blue sleep eyes/Molded lashes. Rooted dark blonde hair. Pierced ears. Painted fingernails and toes. Marks: Ideal Toy Corp/VT-10½ on head. 1957. $14.00.

Ideal - 14" "Toni". All hard plastic with glued on red nylon wig. Blue sleep eyes/lashes. Closed mouth. Open hands with index and little fingers extended above others. Marks: Ideal Doll/Made In USA on head. Ideal Doll/P-90 on body. Dress Tag: Genuine Toni Doll with nylon wig Made By Ideal Toy Corp. 1949. $20.00.

RDF - 3½" "Tiny Tim". All vinyl in sitting position. Unjointed. Very long nose. Glued on long mohair. Felt eyes. Marks: RDF '67, on foot. 1967. $8.00.

LJN - 7½" "Mike, Terry and Willie of the Rookies". Plastic and vinyl. Fully jointed. Marks: ⨍ℓ LJN Toys/Hong Kong. 1974. $3.00 each.

LJN - 7½" "John and Roy of the TV Emergency Squad". Plastic and vinyl. Completely jointed. Torso, under jointed waist is actually molded white jockey shorts. Slightly open/closed mouth with unpainted teeth area. Original. Made in 1973 for the 1974 marked. Marks: ⨍ℓ LJN Toys Ltd/Hong Kong/All Rights Reserved. Brown molded hair and painted blue eyes. $3.00 each.

Dutchess - 7" "Roy Rogers & Dale Evans". All hard plastic. Roy: Blue sleep eyes. Dale: Brown sleep eyes. Both original. Marks: Dutchess Doll Corp/Design Copyright/1948, on back. $5.00 each.

Lenci - 11" Felt. All original. Pre-World War II. 11" - $75.00.

Societe Francaise de Frabrication de Bebes et Jouets - 19" Socket head. Open mouth. Made after 1899. 19" $325.00.

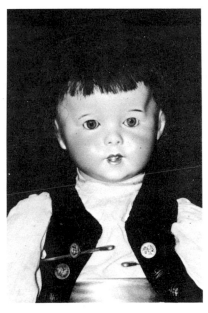

Jumeau - 16" "Poupee Parisienne". Closed mouth. smiling. Wood body and limbs. Marks: E, on head. These dolls are referred to as "Mona Lisa". (Wood) 16" - $1,100.00

Societe Francaise De Fabrication De Bebes et Jouets - 24" "Twirp" 15" head. Cir. blue sleep eyes. Open/closed mouth/2 molded teeth on rim. Socket head. Marks: 23/France/S.F.B.J./ 247/Paris/11. 24" - $1,800.00.

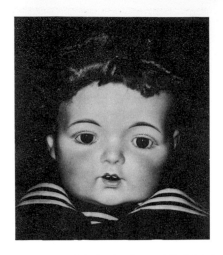

Fulpher - 31" Socket head on a fully jointed composition body. Open mouth. Marks: $325.00.

Fulpher - The Fulpher Pottery Co. began in 1805 but only made dolls heads for a short time between 1918 and 1921. These heads were developed, first, for the Horsman Doll Co. Fulpher also made some all bisque "Kewpies" in 1920 and "Peterkin", an all bisque, in 1919. Marks:

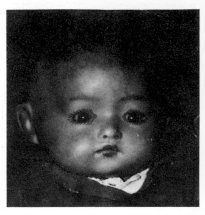

Steiner, Herm - 12" Brown bisque baby. Sleep eyes and closed mouth. Marks: 11/ Germany. ($225.00.

Steiner, Hermann-Hermann Steiner did not enter the doll field until after World War 1 (1921) and made dolls at Neustadt, near Colburg and Sonneberg. Sample marks:

The following are some of Herm Steiner's mold numbers: 45, 75, 128, 133, 134, 140, 141, 145, 401, 947, 4015, 4016, 95464 (this is a registration number incised on some dolls)

Rag Dolls - 17½" Rag doll of the 1890's. 17½" - $100.00.

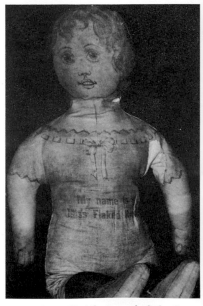

Rag Dolls - 25" All stamped cloth. Cotton filled. Marks: My Name is Miss Flaked Rice, across stomach. 25" - $45.00.

Wax - 16½" Wax over papier mache. Sleep eyes. 16½" - $225.00.

Manufacturer Unknown - 33" German composition of 1885. Closed mouth. Glass eyes. Cloth body. 33" - $200.00.

Parian - 24½" Pink Parian "Dolly Madison" with molded upper and lower lids. Made at Grosbreitenbach by Macheleidt. Marks: 8 24½" - $650.00

Papier Mache - 30" Blonde mache with blue eyes and very deep (long) shoulder plate. Cloth body with leather arms. $400.00.

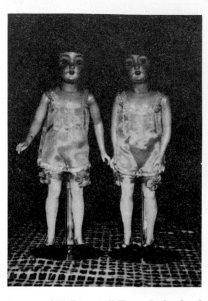

Papier Mache - 6½" All painted papier mache. Molded bust. Jointed shoulders and hips. ca. 1890's. Marks: none. 6½" - $125.00

Simon and Halbig - 14" Twins Socket head with shapely 5 piece bodies. All original. Teddies of silk crepe, stockings, garters and patent shoes. Original box marked 1/12 doz. 2/382/33/Made in Germany. Childhood dolls of Jennie Gregg and sister. $175.00.

Wax - 18½" French wax fashion type. Glass eyes. Pierced ears. 18½" - $300.00.

China - 13½" - Rare black hairdo with molded flowers and pierced ears. Germany. 13½" - $200.00.

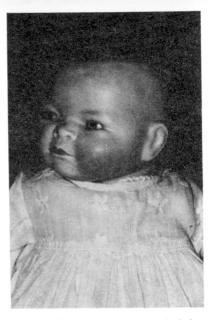

Simon & Halbig - 14" Socket head. Open mouth. Marks: 1329/Germany/Simon Halbig/ S&H. Oriental. 14" - $850.00.

Grace S. Putnam - 14½" long Bye-Lo baby. Cloth body. Celluloid hands. Marked on back. 14½" - $325.00.

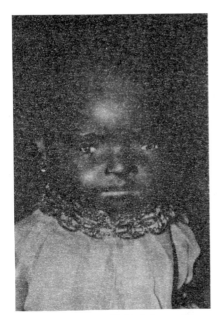

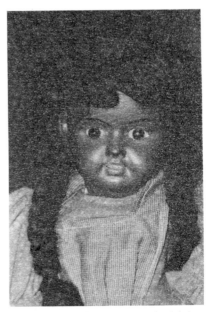

Heubach, Ernst - 8½" Dark brown bisque head on 5 piece brown baby body. Set glass eyes, closed mouth and pierced ears. Marks: Heubach Koppelsdorf/399. 14/0D.R.G.M./- Germany. $225.00.

Simon and Halbig - 14" Brown socket head on brown fully jointed body. Open mouth. Marks: 50 9/0/5/Made in Germany. Second one marked 50 9/0/S.H./Germany. $175.00.

Kestner - 10" "Gibson" Shoulder plate. Sleep eyes. All original. Marks: G-0/172/Made In Germany. ca. 1910. $650.00.

Kestner - 25". Turned Shoulder plate. Open mouth/4 teeth. Marks: J.D.K./12/147. 25" - $225.00.

Kestner - 25" Socket head. Original. Marks: h½ Made in 12/Germany/167. ca. 1892. $325.00.

Kestner - 14" Molded eyebrows. Unpierced ears. Set brown eyes. Marks: B Made in 6/Germany/169. ca. 1892. $550.00.

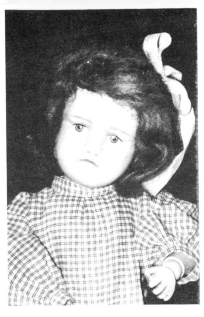

Steiner, Jules Nichols - 10" Socket head on crude 5 piece mache body. Set eyes. Closed mouth. Marks: Steiner/Paris/FR-A-3. $550.00

Schoenhut - 16" All wood. Brown decal eyes. Label seal on chest: Schoenhut Doll/Pat. Jan. 17th 1911/USA. All original. 16" - $225.00.

Heirnich Handwerck - 17" Shoulder plate. Kid body. Open mouth. Marks:HcH5/OH ∞ . 17" - $150.00.

Rabery & Delphieu - 17" Socket head. Closed mouth. Marks: R.OD. 17" - $800.00.

All Bisque - 6½". All bisque with one piece
body and head. Open mouth. Blue sleep eyes
with hair lashes. Open crown. Painted on
shoes and socks. Original. $200.00.

All Bisque - 4½" All bisque. Sleep eyes. Closed
mouth. Molded on hose and black Mary Janes.
Jointed shoulders and hips. Marks: 150. Kestner seal on chest. $70.00.

Simon & Halbig - 28" Socket head. Adult
body. Sleep eyes/lashes. Open mouth. Marks:
30/130.28" - $400.00.

Rabery & Delphieu - 20" Socket head. Closed
mouth. Marks: R.ID. 20" - $900.00.

Simon & Halbig - 20" Socket head. Pierced ears. Sleep eyes/lashes. Marks: Dep. 20" - $400.00.

Kammer & Reinhardt - 17" Socket head. Marks: K ✡ R/Simon Halbig. 17" - $175.00.

Schoenau & Hoffmeister - 30½" Socket head. Sleep eyes/lashes. Open mouth. Marks: ☆ : H/1906. $125.00.

Union Nationale Inter-Syndicali-22" Socket head. Open mouth. Marks: 71 Unis 149/France/60. The Unis France is in an oval. $125.00.

E. Denamur - 15" Socket head. Closed mouth. Marks: E.6D./Depose. 15" - $800.00.

Kely & Hahn - 23" Socket head. Registered in 1902. Marks: 250/KH/Walkure/3¼/Germany. $275.00.

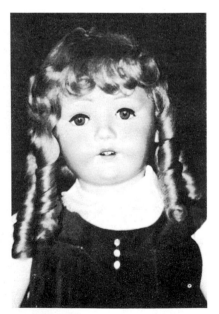

Max Oscar Arnold - 33" Socket head. Open mouth. Marks: ⬡ /200/Welsch/Made In Germany. Made in 1922 for the Welsch Co. $250.00.

Armand Marseille - 17½" Shoulder plate. Kidolene body. Molded eyebrows. Open mouth. Marks: Germany/Mabel/3/0. $75.00.

J.D. Kestner - 32" Socket head. Unpierced ears. Marks: M½ 16½/164. ca. 1895. 12" - $325.00.

Bru - 18" Socket head on bisque shoulder plate. Closed mouth. Kid body with bisque lower arms. Marks: 11, on head, Bru Jne R, on shoulder plate. 18" - $2,300.00.

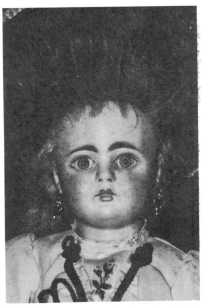

Belton - 15" Concave head with 3 holes. Socket head on wood/composition fully jointed body. Open/closed mouth. All original. Ears pierced into head. Marks: None. $400.00

Union Nationale Inter-Syndicali - 24 Socket head. Sleep eyes/lashes. Open mouth. Marks: Unis/70, on head. Body marked Jumeau. 24" - $275.00.

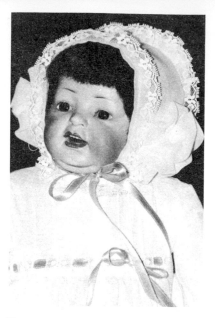

Ernst Heubach - 19½" Baby. Marks: Heubach-Kippelsdorf/320-6/6/Germany 19½" - $175.00.

Kestner - 20" Open mouth/4 teeth. Molded tongue. Dimples. Marks: 152. ca. 1912. $325.00.

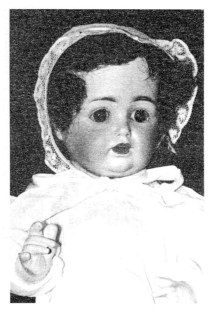

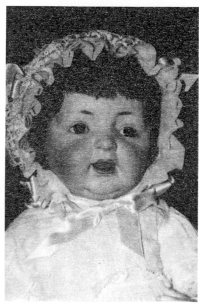

Kestner - 16" Open mouth. Marks: JDK/260/Germany/48. ca. 1912. $175.00

Kestner - 18" Socket head on 5 piece composition bent baby leg body. Open mouth with molded tongue. Set brown eyes. Marks: J.D.K./236. $325.00.

Half Dolls - 2¾" Yellow blonde. White and lime green dress. Pink flowers. Marks: Japan. $7.00.

Half Dolls - 2¼" White with orange trim with blue bows. Grey hair. Green/brown flowers. Marks: Germany/11370. $15.00.

Half Dolls 3¼" Blonde hair. Rose dress with blue hat and collar. Red tie. Marks: Made in/Japan, high on head. $8.00.

Half Dolls - 3½" White with rose checks on dress. Orange bow and hat: Blue feather, cuffs and collar. Marks: Japan. $8.00.

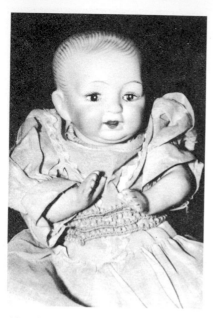

Manufacturer Unknown - 6" Baby with brush stroke hair. Open mouth. Painted teeth and eyes. Marks: 3-4-10. 6" - $50.00.

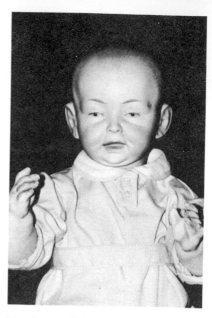

Manufacturer Unknown - 15" Molded brush stroke hair. Painted blue eyes. Open/closed mouth. Marks: 2/Germany. 15" - $225.00.

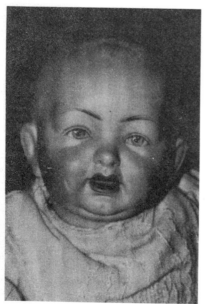

Kestner - 11" Socket head on 5 piece bent leg baby body. Full open/closed mouth. Intaglio painted eyes. Marks: 142/J.D.K. $425.00.

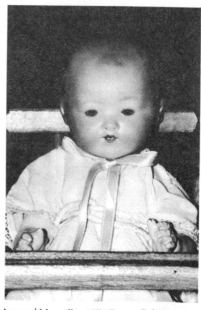

Armand Marseille - 16" "Dream Baby". Open mouth version. Marks: A.M./Germany/351/ 2½K. Made for the Arranbee Doll Co. 1924. $225.00.

Cameo - 11" Kewpie. Composition with jointed shoulders. 11" - $55.00.

Cameo - 13" "Kewpie" All composition. Fully jointed. Original. 13" - $65.00.

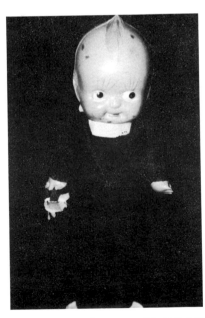

All Bisque - 5" Googly. Jointed shoulders and hips. Closed mouth, painted on shoes and socks and original wig. Marks: None. $295.00.

Manufacturer Unknown - 3" Celluloid Preacher. Jointed arms only. Marks: Made In Japan. 3" - $30.00.

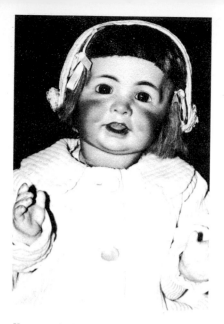

Kammer & Reinhardt - 17" Socket head. Movable tongue. Original wig. Marks: K ✡ R/Simon Halbig/116a/42. 17" - $700.00.

Armand Marseille - 23" "My Dearie" for George Borgfeldt 1908 to 1922. Shoulder plate. Marks: Armand Marseille/390n/DR GM/246/1/A.6M. 23 - $225.00.

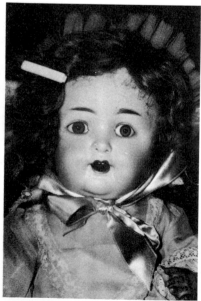

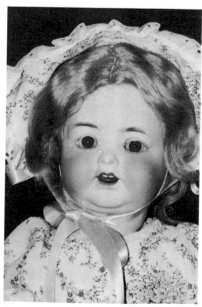

Schuetzmeister and Quendt - 17" Socket head on 5 piece bent leg baby body. Sleep eyes. Open mouth with two upper teeth. Marks: ⌀ /Germany. $225.00.

Heubach, Ernst - 18" Socket head on 5 piece Toddler body. Sleep eyes, open mouth with teeth and "tremble" tongue. Marks: Heubach Koppelsdorf/342-d. $325.00.

All Bisque - 6" All bisque. Jointed shoulders only. Marks: 665:D/Germany/15. $32.50.

All Bisque - 5½" Tie on arms. Molded hairband-type. 1917-1930. $16.00.

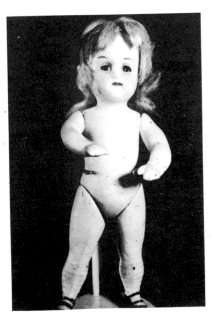

All Bisque - 5" All bisque with open crown. Glass eyes. Jointed hips and shoulders. Molded on shoes/socks. Marks: 2/0 Germany/3547. $65.00.

All Bisque - 8" Nicer quality bisque. Deeply molded hair. Delicately tinted features. Tied on arms. Marks: Japan and symbol. ca. 1915. $22.00.

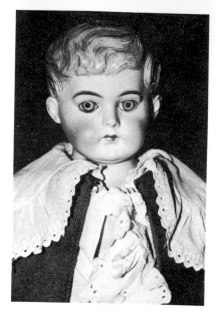

Manufacturer Unknown - - 16½" baby.
Marks:BG (or 86)   ## /Nippon. 16½" -
$125.00

Parian - 17" Parian with glass eyes. Side part
boy's hair do. 17" - $435.00

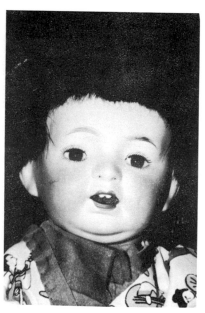

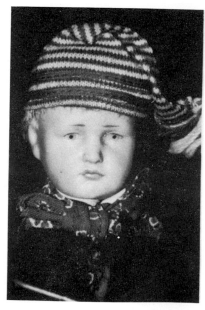

Japan - 12" Socket head on 5 piece baby body.
Open mouth/2 upper teeth. Ca. 1918. Marks:
✳ /Japan. Made for the Morimura
Brothers of New York. $125.00.

Kammer and Rinehardt - 6" Peter. Socket
head on composition/mache 5 piece body.
Painted blue eyes. Closed pouty mouth.
Marks: K ✡ R/101. Original clothes.
$700.00.

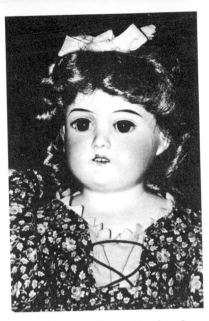

Simon & Halbig - 21" Socket head. Pierced ears. Marks: S&H 1079/Dep/Germany/8. $225.00.

Armand Marseille - 20" Shoulder plate. Open mouth. Kid body. Marks: Floradora/A.O.M./ Made in Germany. 20" - $125.00.

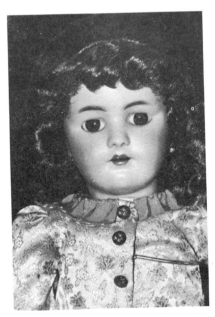

Heinrich Handwerck - 22" Socket head. Open mouth. Marks: Germany/Heinrich Handwerck/Simon & Halbig. 22" - $250.00.

Armand Marseille - 20" Socket head. Molded eyebrows. Open mouth. Marks: Made In Germany/A4M. $175.00.

Ernst Heubach - 18" Shoulder plate. Kid body. Open mouth. Marks: 3095. 18" - $175.00.

Kestner - 19" Socket head character. Open mouth/2 teeth. Marks: Made in 12/Germany/143. Body: Germany/2. ca. 1892. $225.00.

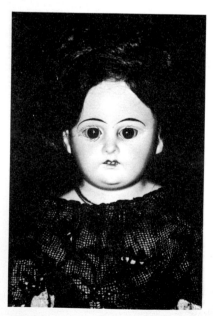

Armand Marseille - 17" Lady doll. Shoulder plate. Kid body. Open mouth. Marks: 1894/A.M.2/0 Dep. 11½" - $175.00.

Simon & Halbig - 19½" Shoulder plate. Kid body. Open mouth. Marks:S.H.1010. This is the head they later used on the Edison Phonograph doll (1889). 19½" $225.00.

Edmund Ulrich Steiner - 21" Shoulder plate.
marks: 25.5/6 170 K/Germany. 21" $175.00.

Kestner - 17½" Socket head on an adult body.
Marks: D Made in 8/Germany/162. 17½" -
$375.00.

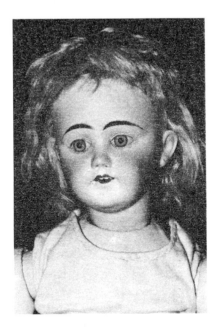

Societe Francaise de Fabrication de Bebes et
Jouets - 17½" Socket head. Open mouth. Set
eyes. Pierced ears. Marks: S.F.B.J./Paris. Body
marked Jumeau. 17½" - $325.00.

Manufacturer Unknown - 20¼" Socket head.
Unjointed wrists. French body. Open mouth.
Paperweight eyes. Marks: none. 20" - $375.00.

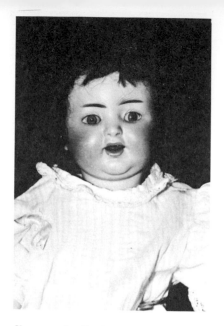

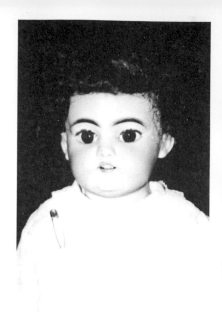

Kammer & Reinhardt - 13½". Open mouth/upper teeth. Sleep eyes. Marks K ✡ R/Simon Halbig/126. 13½" - $325.00.

Simon & Halbig - 22" Shoulder plate/kid. Almond shaped eyes/lashes. Marks: Dep/Wimpern/Gesetzel Schutz/SH1080-8. Wimpern means "eyelashes". 22" - $225.00.

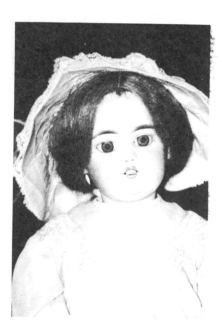

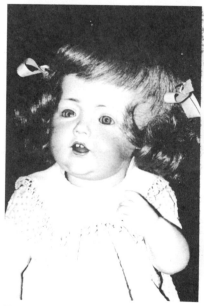

Simon & Halbig - 21" Socket head. Marks: S.H. 1079 3½/Dep. $225.00.

Kestner - 14" "Hilda". Open crown/wig. Marks: G Made in Germany 11/245/J.D.K. Jr./1914/Hilda $550.00.

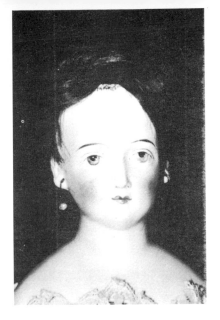

Manufacturer Unknown - 18" Wood bodied fashion with jointed ankles. Marks: 4, high on head. 18" - $1,600.00.

Parian - 18" Bald parian with wig. Pierced ears and molded painted eyes. Cloth body with parian arms. $650.00.

China - 23" Adelaide Patti of the 1870's. 10 sausage curls and brush strokes over ears. Cloth body with china limbs. $450.00.

Parian - 14" parian of the "Dolly Madison" style. Molded in blue with gold trim ribbon. Glass inset eyes. $795.00.

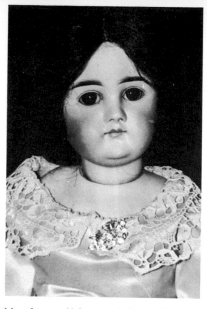

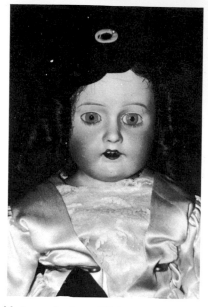

Manufacturer Unknown - 21" Swivel head on bisque shoulder plate. Closed mouth. Marks: 8, on head. 21" - $550.00.

Morimura Brothers - 22" Socket head. Lashes painted below eyes only. Open mouth. Marks: 5/ ⊛ /Japan. 22" - 175.00.

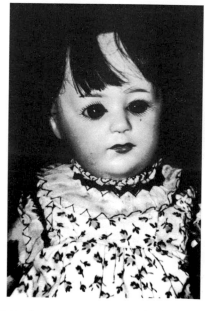

Manufacturer Unknown - 10½" Socket head Open/closed mouth. Marks: none. 10½" - $375.00.

Gebruder Heubach - 12" Socket head. Glass eyes. Closed mouth. Original. Marks: 3/3420 12" - $500.00.

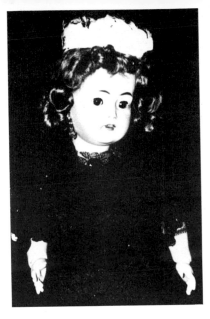

Recknagel - 14" Socket head. Open mouth. Marks: 1909/Eep/R5/OA/13. 14" - $125.00.

Kammer & Reinhardt - 20" Flirty brown eyes/lashes. Open mouth. Marks: K ✡ R/S & H/117n. 20" - $325.00.

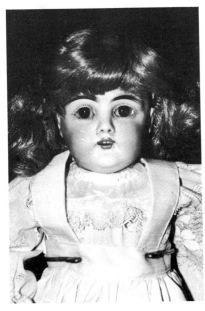

All Bisque - 5½" All bisque with swivel head. Set in glass eyes. Closed mouth. Marks: 5 2/3. $100.00.

Kestner - 17" Socket head. Open mouth. Very flat head in back. Marks: DR 154 5½. $225.00.

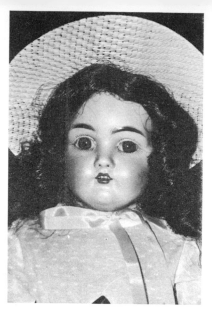

Kestner - 17" Shoulder plate. Kid body. Open mouth. Marks: 5¾. 154. Dep./Made In Germany. 12" - $225.00, 26" - $275.00.

Kestner - 25" Socket head. Marks: Made in/Germany/171, on head. Body: Excelsior/Germany/ 2. 12" - $75.00, 26" - $225.00.

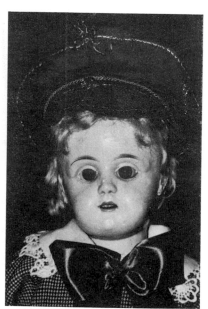

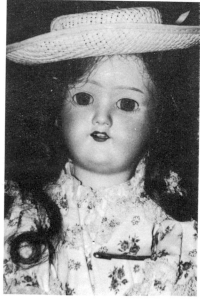

Metal - 20" Tin head with inset blue glass eyes. Open mouth and crown. Original wig. Ears are applied after the head was put together. Fully jointed German composition/wood body. Marks: None. $87.50.

Japan - 17" Socket head on fully jointed composition body. Open mouth, blue sleep eyes with lashes painted below eyes only. Marks: ⊛ /Japan. Made for Morimura Bros. N.Y. $175.00.

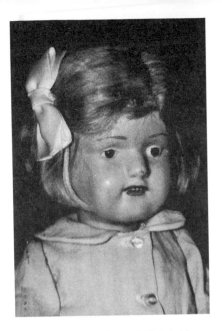

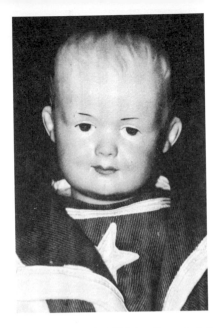

Schoenhut - 14" All wood. Painted brown eyes. Open/closed mouth with painted upper teeth. Original wig. Marks: seal-see introduction. Not repainted - $285.00.

Marseille, Armand - 15" Infant Berry. Socket head on fully jointed composition/wood body. Closed mouth, intaglio blue eyes, molded blonde hair. Marks: 500/Germany/A 1 M with DRGM running vertically down side of mark. Made in 1909. $300.00.

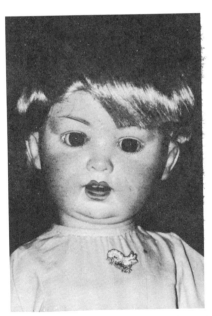

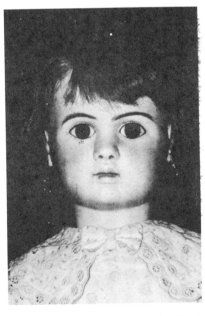

Reinecke, Otto - 18" Sleep eyes, dimples and open mouth with two upper teeth and molded tongue. 5 piece bent leg baby body. Marks: PM/914/8. Ca. 1910. $265.00.

Steiner, Jules Nichols - 25" Socket head. Closed mouth. Pierced ears. Marks: A 17/ Paris, on head. Le Parisian SGDG/stamp in red on body. $1,495.00.

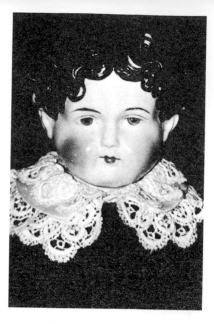

China - 19" Blonde China with bangs. Called "Highland Mary" by collectors. 19" $325.00.

China - 29" Black hair China. Exposed ears. Molded eyelids. 29" - $350.00.

All Bisque - 7" All bisque girl with side part pale blonde hair and molded in ribbon. One piece body and head. $115.00.

White Bisque - 9½" White stone bisque. Cloth body and upper limbs. Stone bisque lower arms and legs. Painted eyes. Marks: 114/10/0, on shoulder. 9½" - $80.00.

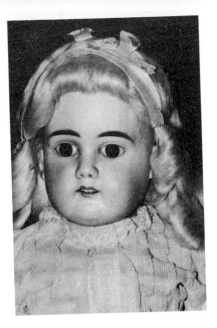

Jumeau - 25" Open mouth. Marks: 1907/10.
Marked Jumeau body. 25" - $475.00.

Steiner, Edmund Ulrich - 24" Shoulder head
on kid body with bisque arms. Open mouth.
Marks: ◇ /Made in Germany. $225.00

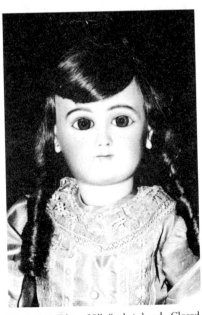

Manufacturer Unknown - 20" Shoulder plate.
Open mouth. Kid body. Unpierced ears.
Marks: 7.20" - $175.00.

Schmitt & Fils - 20" Socket head. Closed
mouth. Marks: 10/ ⊗ .20" - $1,800.00.

Half Doll - 2½" China. Beautifully made with arms extended. Marks: Germany 58882. ca. 1920. $25.00.

Gaultier, Fernand - 25" Socket head with portrait eyes. Pierced ears and straight wrists. Open/closed mouth. Pink wash over the dark rimmed eyes. Marks: F5G, on Jumeau marked body. $1,050.00.

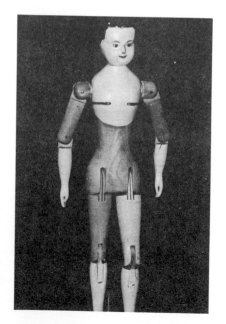

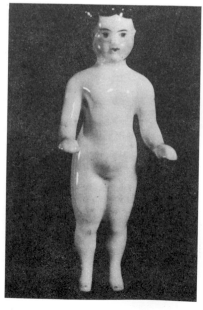

Wood - 18" Springfield wood of the Ellis type. 18" - $495.00

Frozen Charlotte - 5" Marks: 100 on back. 5" - $100.00.

FOR MORE INFORMATION ON DOLLS

MODERN COLLECTOR'S DOLLS I, II, III
by Patricia Smith

This series is considered the finest identification and value guide ever produced. Each book features some 1200 different photographs and up to 2000 current values making the three book series a must for the advanced doll collector and dealer. Dolls from 1935 through 1976 are included in this series with a total of 3600+ photographs and 5000+ values. There are no duplicates in any of the three volumes.

MODERN COLLECTOR'S DOLLS $17.95

MODERN COLLECTOR'S DOLLS SECOND SERIES $17.95

MODERN COLLECTOR'S DOLLS THIRD SERIES...... $17.95

MODERN COLLECTOR'S DOLLS Three Volume Set $52.50

ANTIQUE COLLECTOR'S DOLLS I & II
by Patricia Smith

Another popular series by Patricia Smith features dolls from 1850 through 1935. Each book contains about 1200 dolls with photographs and 2000 current values. Patricia Smith is probably the most popular doll author today with ten titles to her credit. There are no duplicates in either of the books.

ANTIQUE COLLECTOR'S DOLLS $17.95

ANTIQUE COLLECTOR'S DOLLS Second Series $17.95

ANTIQUE COLLECTOR'S DOLLS Two volume Set $35.00

Ask for these at your favorite bookstore
or
Order from

COLLECTOR BOOKS
P.O. Box 3009
Paducah, Kentucky 42001